Contents

Answers to the questions are on the back of the Pull-out Poster in the centre of the book.

This book covers unit 3E from the year three scheme of work

Published by Coordination Group Publications Ltd.

CONTRIBUTORS:

Taissa Csáky	Becky May
Chris Dennett	Katherine Reed
Dominic Hall	Claire Thompson
Tim Major	James Paul Wallis

ISBN: 978 1 84146 252 3
Groovy website: www.cgpbooks.co.uk
Jolly bits of clipart from CorelDRAW®
Printed by Elanders Hindson Ltd, Newcastle upon Tyne.

With thanks to Christine Tinkler and Glenn Rogers for the proofreading.

<u>Push and Pull</u>

It's not always easy to tell whether something's pushing or pulling.

Q1 Draw lines to join each label with the right picture.

pulling	nothing happening	pushing

Q2 Each picture shows a push or a pull. Write 'PUSHING' or 'PULLING' in the gaps.

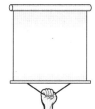

The hand is .... the blind.

The boy's foot is .... the skateboard.

The monk is .... the rope.

The finger is .... the doorbell.

The books are .... on the bookend.

<u>I like this page — it's a pushover...</u>

This book's about magnets and springs. Magnets and springs can push <u>and</u> pull.
It's useful to be able to spot pushes and pulls when you're looking at magnets and springs.

Attract and Repel

Magnets are special. You can feel forces just by putting them near each other.

Q1 The pictures show what happened when I held 2 magnets together and then let go.
What is the scientific word for what the magnets did? Tick (✓) the correct word.

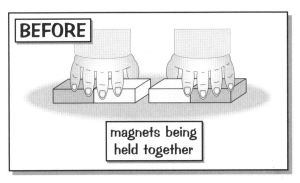

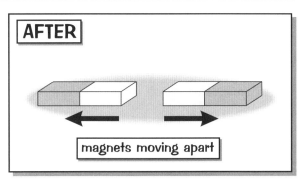

rope ☐   attract ☐   attack ☐   repel ☑

Q2 The pictures show what happened when I held 2 magnets together and then let go.
What is the scientific word for what the magnets did? Tick (✓) the correct word.

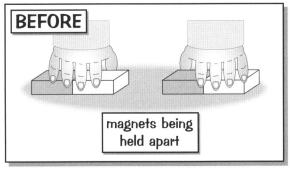

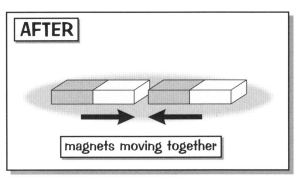

rope ☐   attract ☐   attack ☐   repel ☑

Q3 Fill in the blanks to finish off the sentences about magnets.
Choose from the words on the blob. Use each word only once.

When magnets pull together, you say they .... each other.

When magnets push apart, you say they .... each other.

repel

attract

Magnets — *ATTRACT* and *R E P E L...*

If you can get some magnets, have a play with them. They are great fun — and a bit strange.

Attract and Repel

I spy with my little eye, something beginning with 'M'...

Q1   What are the magnets doing in these pictures? Tick (✓) the correct words.

a)
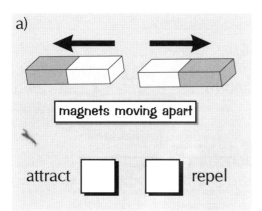
magnets moving apart

attract ☐   ☐ repel

b)
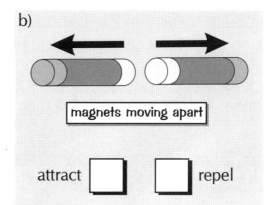
magnets moving apart

attract ☐   ☐ repel

c)
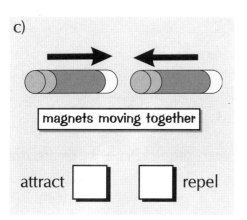
magnets moving together

attract ☐   ☐ repel

d)
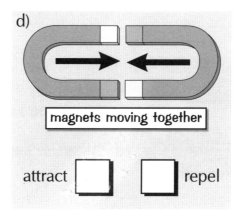
magnets moving together

attract ☐   ☐ repel

Oi! Let me go!

Tom was naughty with his magnet.

Q2   I held these magnets, and they pulled together.
      Then I turned one of the magnets round. What do you think happened?
      Draw in the arrows, then write 'magnets pulling together' or 'magnets pushing apart'.

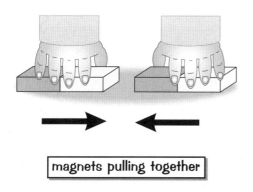
magnets pulling together

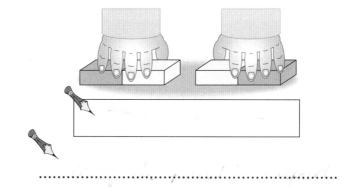

....

Magnets — they're brilliant...

Magnets are really useful. There are magnets to hold the fridge door closed,
magnets used to lift cars, magnets to... well, there is more on that later in the book!

Testing Magnetic Materials

The best way of finding out if objects are magnetic
is to grab a magnet and start holding it near things.

Q1   Ned wants to test some materials to see if they're magnetic.
      Put a tick (✓) next to the best way to find out.

      A material is magnetic if...

      ☐ ...it's attracted   ☐ ...it's attracted to   ☐ ...it can dance
         to a stone.   a magnet.   the conga.

Q2   Ned is confused about the difference between a **magnet** and a **magnetic material**.
      Look at the pictures — then fill in the gaps using words from the wibbly box.

**Magnets attract or
repel each other.**

MAGNETIC   ATTRACTED   ALL   ENDS   MAGNETS

.... can attract or repel each

other. It depends on the ....

that are facing each other. Paper clips are made of

a .... material. They are

.... to the magnet. Magnetic

**Paper clips are attracted
to a magnet.**

materials are attracted to ....

parts of a magnet, not just one end.

Q3   Ned wants to do an investigation to test whether 6 objects are magnetic.
      Put a ⟨circle⟩ round each piece of equipment he'll need.

      a ruler

            a magnet   weighing scales   6 different objects   a funny hat

Testing testing 1 2 3...

I bet you knew all this stuff already. When I was a youngster, the only toys we had
were magnets. Everyone likes playing with magnets (except for robots).

Testing Magnetic Materials

Finding out if something is magnetic is a pretty easy test.
But you've still got to make it a <u>fair test</u>.

Q1 (Circle) the right ending to finish off this sentence about fair tests.

To make a test fair you should change...

...only **one** thing each
time you do the test.

...**two** things each
time you do the test.

...**everything** each
time you do the test.

Q2 Why is it important to make sure the test is **fair**? Tick (✓) the right answer.

☐ So that your results are different from everyone else's results.

☐ So that you know your results are right.

☐ Because fairs are brilliant fun.

Q3 Ned's thinking about how to do the experiment and make it fair. Choose the three correct parts of his method — then write them out on the dotted line.

1. Use different strength magnets to test different objects.   **OR**   Test the objects with the same magnet each time.

2. Don't put the magnet near to the objects.   **OR**   Touch each object with the magnet.

3. If the object is attracted to the magnet then it's **magnetic**.   **OR**   If the object doesn't move then it's **magnetic**.

1. ....

2. ....

3. ....

All the fun of the fair...

It's pretty tricky making an investigation into magnets unfair — but some people manage to get it wrong. Always make sure you do fair tests — because they're ace.

Testing Magnetic Materials

This is the good bit — Ned's been waving his
magnet around, trying to finish his investigation.

Ned has collected 6 objects and now he wants to find out which ones are magnetic.
He's made a prediction and ticked the ones he thinks are magnetic in a table.

Ned's prediction:
All the things made of
metal will be magnetic.

"Prediction" means
a guess at what
will happen.

Copper Kettle

Wooden Spoon

Aluminium Foil

Iron Can

Iron Horseshoe

**Ceramic (pottery)
Mug**

Object	Will it be magnetic?
Copper Kettle	✓
Wooden Spoon	✗
Aluminium Foil	✓
Iron Horseshoe	✓
Ceramic Mug	✗
Iron Can	✓

Q1 Ned put a magnet near each object and wrote down what happened. Use his notes
to finish off the results table — just put ticks (✓) and crosses (✗) in the right places.

Mug: nothing happened.

Spoon: no movement.

Horseshoe: stuck to the magnet.

Kettle: nothing happened.

Can: attracted to the magnet.

Foil: no movement.

Object	Is it magnetic?
Copper Kettle	....
Wooden Spoon	....
Aluminium Foil	....
Iron Horseshoe	....
Ceramic Mug	....
Iron Can	....

I predict that you will soon finish reading this page...

Have a go at testing objects yourself to see if they are magnetic. Test lots of things
including the stuff Ned tested. Guess if each thing will be magnetic before you try it.

Testing Magnetic Materials

Well, that was fun — but if you think that's the end of it then you've got another think coming. Now you need to work out what the test <u>tells</u> you.

Q1 Were all the metal things magnetic? Write YES or NO on the dotted line. ....

Q2 How many of the objects that Ned tested were magnetic?
Put a tick (✓) next to the right answer.

☐ None of the objects were magnetic.

☐ Only the horseshoe and the can were magnetic.

☐ All the metal objects were magnetic.

Q3 What can you say about the materials which were magnetic?
(Circle) the right ending to the sentence.

Out of the 6 objects that Ned tested...

...only the ones made from wood were magnetic.

...only the ones made from copper were magnetic.

...only the ones made from iron were magnetic.

Q4 What conclusion can you make about magnetic materials?
Fill in the gaps using some of the words from the box below.

Objects that are not made from metal are

.... magnetic.

.... metals are magnetic.

.... is a magnetic metal

but .... is a metal

that isn't magnetic.

Ned's robot always wanted to go for walks.

SOME   NOT   CHOCOLATE   COPPER   ALL   IRON

People tell me I have a magnetic personality...

Iron is the only magnetic metal, apart from steel. Steel is magnetic because it is made of <u>iron</u> mixed with other stuff. Steel is used for loads of things like nails and bridges.

Testing Magnets

This investigation is about testing how strong magnets are.
To test how strong a magnet is, you could see how many paper clips it can pick up.

Q1 These magnets are holding as many paper clips as they can.
Which magnet is stronger, A or B? How can you tell? Finish off the sentence below.

I can tell that magnet .... is

stronger because...

....

....

....

(A)

(B)

Q2 For the experiment to work, you have to make it a fair test.
Look at these sentences. Tick (✓) the 3 ideas that will make it a fair test.

All the paper clips must be the same size. ☐

It doesn't matter if the paper clips are different sizes. ☐

Make sure the paper clips hang in a single chain. ☐

Always hold the magnet in your left hand. ☐

Shake the magnet around like a mad thing. ☐

Hold the magnet still. ☐

Life can be hard
for paperclips.

esing magnes — the 't' is stuck on my keyboard...

Did you know — the Earth is a giant magnet. That's why compasses always point north.

Testing Magnets

Have a go at counting some paper clips,
then work out what you'll need to do the investigation.

Q1   Here's a bit of practice. These magnets are holding the most
paperclips they can. Count the paperclips and fill in the table.

Magnet	Number of paperclips it can hold
Ⓐ	
Ⓑ	
Ⓒ	

Finish off this sentence to say which is the strongest magnet.

The strongest magnet is magnet ....

Q2   What will you need to do this investigation?
Choose from the things below — (circle) the ones you will need.

plant

magnet

different-sized
paperclips

magnet

battery

rock

metal cans

magnet

same-sized
paper clips

monkey

What do metal parrots eat? — magnuts...

Enough getting ready. The next page is about <u>doing</u> this investigation — on your marks...

MINI-PROJECT

Testing Magnets

Now you have to <u>do</u> the investigation from pages 8 and 9
— magnets and paper clips and all that.

[Hint: if you can't do the investigation, use my 'spare results' from the bottom of the page.]

Q1 Get three magnets, and label them X, Y and Z.
Which is biggest? Write X, Y and Z in size order in the spaces below.

.... → .... → ....
        biggest   _smallest_

Q2 Which magnet do you think will be the strongest?

I think magnet .... will be the strongest.

Q3 Test the strength of each magnet. Do this by counting how many paper clips each magnet can hold in a chain. Make sure you follow the ideas you ticked on page 8 to make it a fair test. Write your results in the table below.

Magnet	Number of paper clips it can hold
X	
Y	
Z	

Sometimes Mr Jones wished his leg wasn't a giant magnet.

[Spare Results: Magnet X — 3 paper clips; Magnet Y (smallest) — 5 paper clips; Magnet Z (biggest) — 2 paper clips.]

What did the magnet say to the paper clip?...

It can be useful to say what you <u>think</u> will happen at the start of an investigation
— at the end, you can look back and see if you were right or wrong.

Testing Magnets

MINI-PROJECT

The table on page 10 tells you how strong the magnets are.
To make it even <u>easier</u> to see what's going on, fill in this bar chart.

Q1   Fill in this bar chart, using the numbers from your table on the last page.

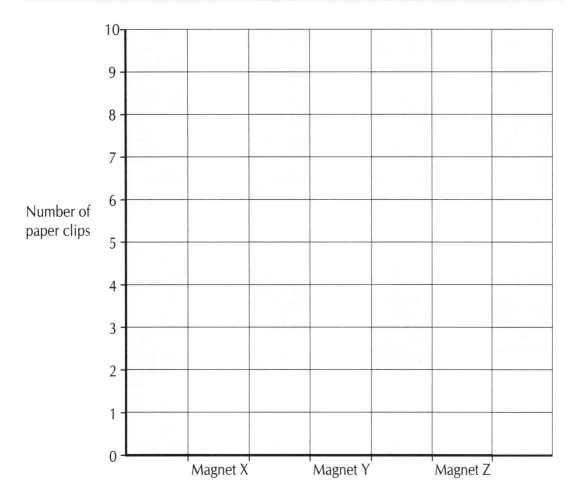

Q2   Write X, Y or Z to finish off these sentences about what you found in the investigation.

Magnet .... was the strongest.   Magnet .... was the weakest.

Q3   Was that what you expected? Tick (✓) YES or NO.
      [Hint: look back at your answer to Q2 on the last page.]

YES ☐   NO ☐

...Let's stick together...

It can be surprising — sometimes the smallest magnet is the strongest one.

Uses of Magnets

Magnets have lots of uses. We use them at home and at work. Best of all — they help us to sort metals for recycling. So they're good for the environment too.

Q1 Below are some examples of how we use magnets.
Draw arrows to match up the correct labels with the pictures.

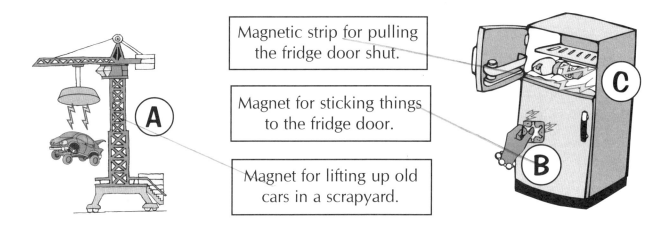

Magnetic strip for pulling the fridge door shut.

Magnet for sticking things to the fridge door.

Magnet for lifting up old cars in a scrapyard.

Q2 Look at the rubbish tip below. The giant magnet attracts iron and steel objects. This helps to pick out metals for recycling. Put a tick (✓) in the box if the magnet will pick up the object.

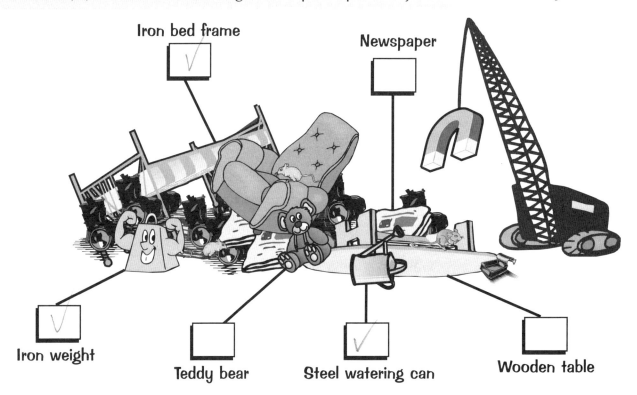

Iron bed frame

Newspaper

Iron weight

Teddy bear

Steel watering can

Wooden table

Magnets — heavy metal fans...

Magnets make life easier. Imagine life without magnets — we would have to crawl through rubbish tips to find metal for recycling and the fridge would never shut properly.

PULL OUT ANSWERS AND POSTER***PULL OUT ANSWERS AND POSTER***PULL OUT ANSWERS AND POSTER***

KS2 Science Answers — Magnets and Springs

Page 14 Forces and Springs

Q1: Sheila is using a **pushing** force to move the car.
Nigel and Dave are using a **pulling** force to get the fish out of the water.

Q2: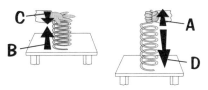

Page 15 Forces and Elastic Bands

Q1: The elastic band is pulling **up** on the hand.
The hand is pulling **down** on the elastic band.

Q2: 'The elastic band will get shorter again' should be ticked.

Q3: When the hand lets go of the elastic band it stops **pulling** down on the band. The only force left is the elastic band pulling **up**. So the **elastic band** moves back upwards and gets **shorter** again.

Page 16 Forces and Everyday Life

Q1: The balloon is **pulling** the boy into the air.
The man is **pushing** down on the tree trunk.
The wrestler is **pushing** the other man away from him.
Fido is **pulling** his kennel.

Q2: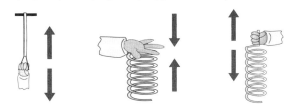
The swimmer is **pulling** the water-skier.

The dog is **pulling** his owner.

The man is **pushing** the boat.

Page 17 Forces Continued

Q1: Forces are either **push** or **pull** actions.
Forces always go in one **direction**.

Q2: When you pull down on an elastic band, the elastic pulls **up** on your hand.
When you push down on a spring, the spring **pushes** up against your hand.
When you pull up on a spring, the spring pulls **down** on your hand.

Q3: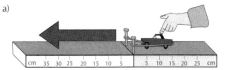

Page 18 Stretching Elastic Bands

Q1: 'The school field is too bumpy — a flat surface would be better' and 'the same toy car should be used for the whole experiment' should be ticked.

Page 19 Stretching Elastic Bands

Q1: a)
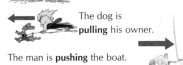

b) The amount the elastic band is stretched is measured on the **grey** ruler. The distance the car has travelled is measured on the **white** ruler. The elastic band should be put round **the nails**. The elastic band should be pulled back with the **car**.

Q2: Prediction 1 should be ticked.

Page 20 Stretching Elastic Bands

Q1:

Distance stretched:	0	5	10	15	20
Distance moved:	**0**	**10**	**15**	**25**	**35**

Q2: The car moved most when the elastic band was pulled back **20 cm**.
The car didn't move at all when the elastic band was pulled back **0 cm**.
The more the elastic band was stretched, the **further** the car went.
The more the elastic band was stretched, the **bigger** its force.
The bigger the **force** of the elastic band, the further the car went.

Page 21 Stretching Elastic Bands

Q1: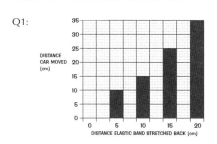

Q2: a) Prediction 1 should be ticked.
b) Depends on whether you predicted correctly on page 19!

Page 22 Making a Concept Map

Q1: Guinea pigs and rabbits are good at jumping — ✗
Guinea pigs are furry — ✓
Guinea pigs have big ears — ✗
Rabbits and guinea pigs are furry — ✓

Q2: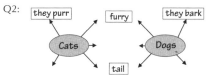

Page 23 A Forces Concept Map

Q1: Clockwise from top:
When you push on a spring it **pushes** back in the opposite direction.
When magnets pull together we say they **attract** each other.
Iron and steel are pulled towards **magnets**.
When you pull on an elastic band, it **pulls** back in the **opposite** direction.
Pushes and pulls are **forces**.
When you push on a spring you **compress** it.
When magnets push apart we say they **repel** each other.

Page 24 Revision Questions

Q1: Forces **push** or **pull**. They only act in one **direction**.

Q2: The magnets are **repelling** each other.   The magnets are **attracting** each other.

Q3: A magnetic material will **move towards** a magnet.

Q4: The **Iron Screw** and **Steel Can** should be ticked.

Q5: All metals are magnetic — **false**
Some metals are magnetic — **true**
Iron and steel are magnetic — **true**
Copper and aluminium are magnetic — **false**

Q6: You can pick out the iron and steel materials because they are attracted to magnets.

Page 25 Revision Questions

Q7: Any 2 reasonable answers e.g. car and bike suspension, in mattresses, pogo sticks, pens, staplers, forcemeters.

Q8: When the hand **pulls** up on the spring, the spring pulls **down** on the hand. When the hand **pushes** down on the spring, the spring pushes **up** on the hand.

Q9: a) The forces are **pull** forces.
b) The further the band is stretched, the **bigger** its force will be.

Q10: The second car should be ticked.

PULL OUT ANSWERS AND POSTER***PULL OUT ANSWERS AND POSTER***PULL OUT ANSWERS AND POSTER***

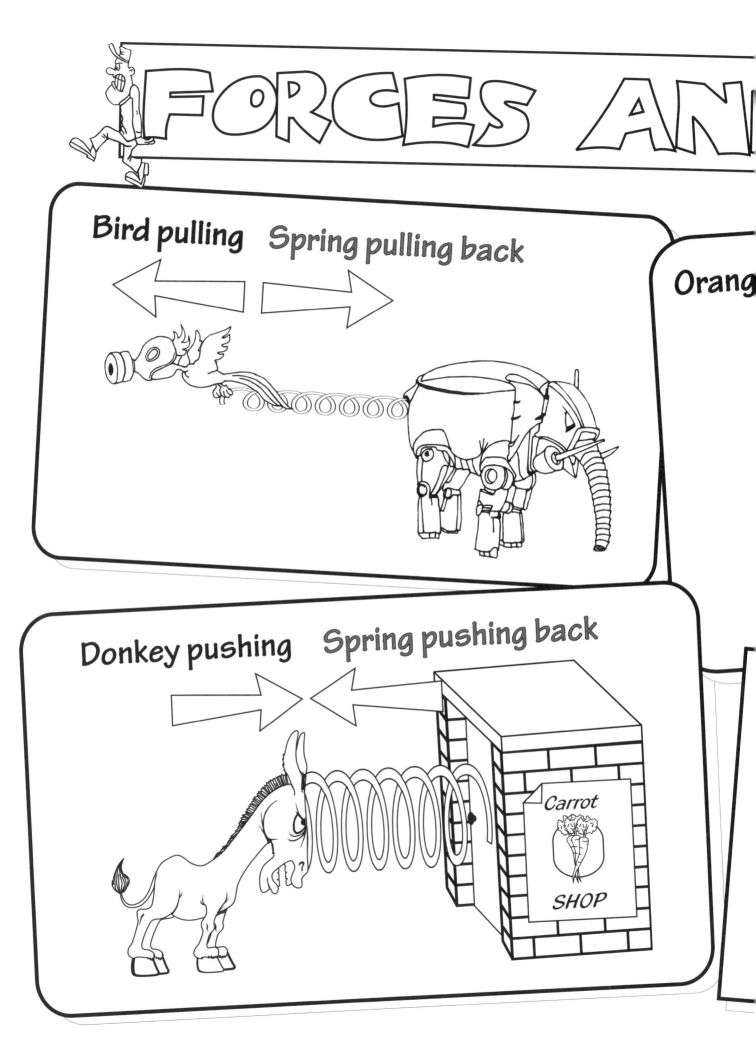

MAGNETS

...tan pulling   Elastic band pulling back

Iron and steel objects are attracted to magnets.

— Magnets and Springs

KS2 Science Answers — Magnets and Springs

Page 1 Push and Pull

Q1:

Q2: The hand is **pulling** the blind.
The boy's foot is **pushing** the skateboard.
The monk is **pulling** the rope.
The finger is **pushing** the doorbell.
The books are **pushing** on the bookend.

Page 2 Attract and Repel

Q1: 'Repel' should be ticked.
Q2: 'Attract' should be ticked.
Q3: When magnets pull together, you say they **attract** each other.
When magnets push apart, you say they **repel** each other.

Page 3 Attract and Repel

Q1: a) Repel   b) Repel
c) Attract   d) Attract

Q2:

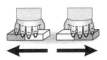

— Magnets pushing apart.

Page 4 Testing Magnetic Materials

Q1: '...it's attracted to a magnet' should be ticked.
Q2: **Magnets** can attract or repel each other. It depends on the **ends** that are facing each other. Paperclips are made of a **magnetic** material. They are **attracted** to the magnet. Magnetic materials are attracted to **all** parts of a magnet, not just one end.
Q3: 'A magnet' and '6 different objects' should be circled.

Page 5 Testing Magnetic Materials

Q1: '...only **one** thing each time you do the test' should be circled.
Q2: 'So that you know your results are right' should be ticked.
Q3: 1. Test the objects with the same magnet each time.
2. Touch each object with the magnet.
3. If the object is attracted to the magnet then it's magnetic.

Page 6 Testing Magnetic Materials

Q1: Only the **Iron Horseshoe** and the **Iron Can** should have ticks next to them.

Page 7 Testing Magnetic Materials

Q1: No
Q2: 'Only the horseshoe and the can were magnetic' should be ticked.
Q3: '...only the ones made from iron were magnetic' should be circled.
Q4: Objects that are not made from metal are **not** magnetic. **Some** metals are magnetic. **Iron** is a magnetic metal but **copper** is a metal that isn't magnetic.

Page 8 Testing Magnets

Q1: I can tell that magnet **B** is stronger because **it can lift more paper clips than magnet A.** (Or equivalent wording).
Q2: These sentences should be ticked:
'All the paper clips must be the same size.'
'Make sure the paper clips hang in a single chain.'
'Hold the magnet still.'

Page 9 Testing Magnets

Q1: A — 3 paper clips   B — 4 paper clips   C — 1 paper clip
The strongest magnet is magnet **B**.

Q2:

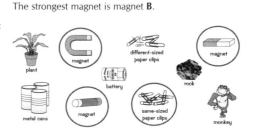

Page 10 Testing Magnets

The answers depend on the magnets used. Using my sample data:
Q1: Magnet Z (biggest) ➜ Magnet X ➜ Magnet Y (smallest)
Q2: I think magnet **Z** will be the strongest.
Q3: Magnet X — 3 paper clips
Magnet Y — 5 paper clips
Magnet Z — 2 paper clips

Page 11 Testing Magnets

The answers depend on the magnets used. Using my sample data:
Q1:

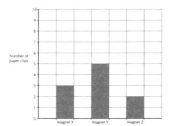

Q2: Magnet **Y** was the strongest. Magnet **Z** was the weakest.
Q3: 'No' should be ticked.

Page 12 Uses of Magnets

Q1: A — Magnet for lifting up old cars in a scrapyard.
B — Magnet for sticking things to the fridge door.
C — Magnetic strip for pulling the fridge door shut.
Q2: 'Iron bed frame', 'iron weight', and 'steel watering can' should all be ticked.

Page 13 Uses of Springs

Q1:

Q2: Any 2 of these ones will do:
Stapler — spring is there so top pops up after stapling.
Bed — springs in mattress give support to people lying on it.
Bike — springs stop the rider bouncing around by taking the impact of bumps.
Car — springs stop the driver bouncing around by taking the impact of bumps.
Forcemeter — you can read off the scale how much a weight pulls against the spring.
Pogo stick — spring bounces so that you are pushed up into the air.
Strongman's spring — man pulls against the spring to get huge muscles.
Pen — spring is there so nib pops back inside when button is pressed.

Uses of Springs

There are springs everywhere. Big springs, small springs... All going 'boing'.

Q1 Draw a (circle) round all the springs you can find in this picture.

puff   pant

Q2 Choose two of the things from the picture above.
For each one, write down **why** the spring is there.

Name of object: ....

Why is the spring there? ....

....

Name of object: ....

Why is the spring there? ....

....

Remember —
you can't play golf
on a pogo stick.

BOINGGGGG...

My favourite spring is a 'Slinky toy' — they can walk down stairs. Weird.

Forces and Springs

A force is either a **PUSH** or a **PULL**.
Forces make things move in different directions.

Q1   Use the words in the box to fill in the blanks
in the sentences below.

Sheila is using a .... force to move the car.

Nigel and Dave are using a .... force to

get the fish out of the water.

Q2   You can show how forces work by using a spring. Put each letter in the correct box
on the diagram to show all the different forces at work.

(A) The hand is pulling up on the spring.   **(C)** The hand is pushing down on the spring.

(B) The spring is pushing up on the hand.   **(D)** The spring is pulling down on the hand.

Be careful — springs are bouncy.
You don't want one
in your eye.

It's time to spring into action...

Forces either <u>push</u> or <u>pull</u> things. Try squashing a spring — it's quite hard work.
That's because there's a force pushing back against you.

Forces and Elastic Bands

Elastic bands are also great for showing us how forces work.
A stretched elastic band is a good example of a <u>pull</u> force.

Q1 Complete the sentences below by putting a
(circle) round the right words in the brackets.

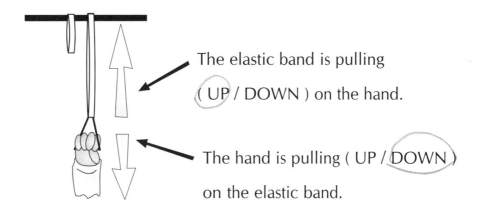

The elastic band is pulling
(UP / DOWN) on the hand.

The hand is pulling (UP / DOWN)
on the elastic band.

Q2 Tick (✓) the right box below to show what you think
will happen when the hand lets go of the elastic band.

Byeeee....
I'm outta here.

☐ The elastic band will get longer.

✓ The elastic band will get shorter again.

☐ The elastic band will grow legs and run away.

Q3 Use the words in the cloud to fill in the blanks in the sentences below.

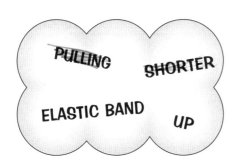

PULLING SHORTER
ELASTIC BAND UP

When the hand lets go of the elastic band it stops
.... down on the band. The only
force left is the elastic band pulling ....
So the .... moves back upwards
and gets .... again.

Stretch your imagination...

I am alive!

You can try stretching an elastic band yourself. Feel how it pulls back up on your hand.
It's weird to think that the elastic has its own force — almost like it's alive...

Forces and Everyday Life

You can't see forces — but that doesn't mean that they're not there. We use forces in everything that we do — from pushing a bike to pulling a tooth out. Amazing.

Q1 For each picture below, write down whether the force is a PUSHING force or a PULLING force.

 The balloon is .... the boy into the air.

 The man is .... down on the tree trunk.

 The wrestler is .... the other man away from him.

 Fido is .... his kennel.

Q2 Now it's your turn.
For each picture draw an arrow showing which direction the force is going in.
Then fill in the gaps to say whether it's a PUSHING force or a PULLING force.

I'm such a nice person — I've done the first one for you.

 The angry duck is ...**PUSHING**... his friend.

 The swimmer is .... the water-skier.

 The dog is .... his owner.

 The man is .... the boat.

Don't push yourself — you'll pull a muscle...

We use forces for <u>everything</u>. Even standing still uses force — because your weight is <u>pushing</u> down on to the floor. Remember that forces always work in one direction.

Forces Continued

Phew — it's the final page about forces. Just a few more questions to check it's all drummed into your brain.

Q1 Fill in the blanks in the sentences below.
This time there are no words for you to choose from.

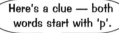

Here's a clue — both words start with 'p'.

Forces are either _ _ _ _ or _ _ _ _ actions.

Forces always go in one _ _ _ _ _ _ _ _ _ .

Look back over pages 14-16 if you get stuck.

Q2 Fill in the blanks to complete the sentences below.

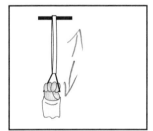

When you **pull down** on an elastic band, the elastic pulls .... on your hand.

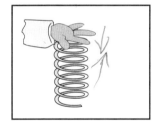

When you **push down** on a spring, the spring .... up against your hand.

When you **pull up** on a spring, the spring pulls .... on your hand.

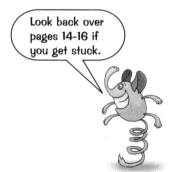

Colin thought he needed _sauce_ to lift the weight.

Q3 Add arrows showing the push and pull forces on the three pictures above. Tip — each picture should have two arrows.

Come on — you can force a smile...

Forces are funny things. They push, they pull and they only go in one direction. You can't _see_ them but you can _feel_ them working. The world of forces is very weird indeed.

Stretching Elastic Bands

You can stretch elastic bands so that they are much longer than usual.
They don't stay that way though — they pull back to their normal shape.

Elsa is doing an experiment — to find out what happens to an elastic band if you stretch it different amounts. She has written down the method for her teacher.

METHOD means how an experiment is going to be done.

EQUIPMENT — nails, tape measure, 5 toy cars, elastic band

METHOD — I will set up the equipment on the school field.

Toy cars will be pulled back in the elastic band and then let go.

I will measure the distance the cars move with a tape measure.

I will stretch back the elastic band a different amount each time.

nails — toy car

elastic band

tape measure

Q1   Elsa's teacher has circled two problems that stop the experiment being a fair test. Tick (✓) two changes Elsa should make.

The experiment should be done in a glass cupboard for her own safety. ☐

The school field is too bumpy — a flat surface would be better. ☐

The same toy car should be used for the whole experiment. ☐

The experiment should be done at different times of day. ☐

The experiment will only work with a real car. ☐

Elsa's teacher would do anything for a bet.

Elastic cars — driving me round the band...

When you stretch an elastic band it will ping back into shape when you let it go.
This means elastic bands can be used as catapults to fling stuff across the room.

Stretching Elastic Bands

Before you do an experiment it's good to guess what the results will be. This is called making a prediction. Then you can compare your prediction with the results.

Q1   a)   Draw an arrow to show the direction the car will move in when Elsa lets go.

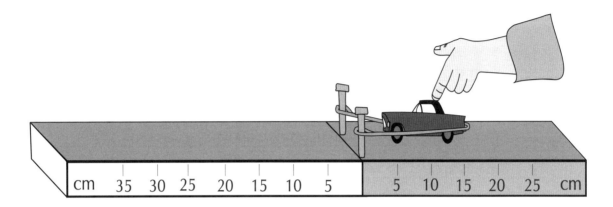

| cm | 35 | 30 | 25 | 20 | 15 | 10 | 5 | | 5 | 10 | 15 | 20 | 25 | cm |

b)   (Circle) the right words to finish off these sentences about the experiment.

The amount the elastic band is stretched is measured on the WHITE / GREY ruler.

The distance the car has travelled is measured on the WHITE / GREY ruler.

The elastic band should be put round THE NAILS / ELSA'S HANDS.

The elastic band should be pulled back with the CAR / RULER.

Q2   Elsa has written down three things she might find out from her experiment.
Tick (✓) the one you agree with.

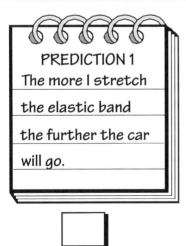

PREDICTION 1
The more I stretch
the elastic band
the further the car
will go.

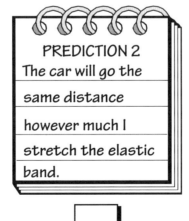

PREDICTION 2
The car will go the
same distance
however much I
stretch the elastic
band.

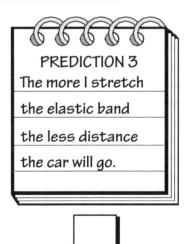

PREDICTION 3
The more I stretch
the elastic band
the less distance
the car will go.

50 twangs — Mozart played by a rubber band...

If you stretch an elastic band in one direction it will pull back in the opposite direction.
Force is a posh word for the pull an elastic band has when it is stretched.

Stretching Elastic Bands

Look for patterns in the results of experiments.
It will help you answer the questions on these two pages.

Q1   Elsa wrote her results quickly into a notepad. Use her results to fill in the table below.

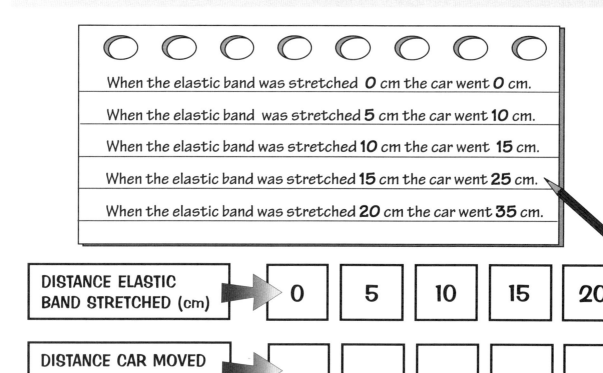

When the elastic band was stretched **0** cm the car went **0** cm.

When the elastic band was stretched **5** cm the car went **10** cm.

When the elastic band was stretched **10** cm the car went **15** cm.

When the elastic band was stretched **15** cm the car went **25** cm.

When the elastic band was stretched **20** cm the car went **35** cm.

DISTANCE ELASTIC BAND STRETCHED (cm)	0	5	10	15	20
DISTANCE CAR MOVED (cm)	....	....	....	....	....

Q2   Complete these sentences using words and numbers from the cars and truck below.

The car moved most when the elastic band was pulled back ....

The car didn't move at all when the elastic band was pulled back ....

The more the elastic band was stretched, the .... the car went.

The more the elastic band was stretched, the .... its force.

The bigger the .... of the elastic band, the further the car went.

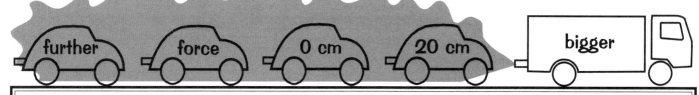

further   force   0 cm   20 cm   bigger

Elastic bands — ARE EVIL, TAKE THEM AWAY...

The amount of force the elastic band has increases the more it is stretched.
The more you stretch the band the further the thing you are catapulting will go.

Stretching Elastic Bands

The final page on elastic bands.

Q1   Complete the bar chart using the results of Elsa's experiment.
I've already filled in the result for 5 cm.

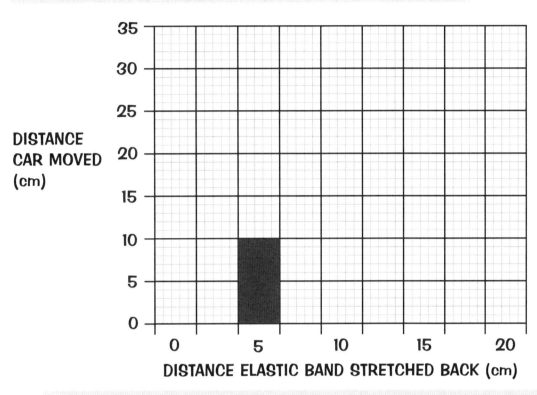

Q2   a)   Look at Elsa's predictions again. Tick (✓) the one that turned out to be right.

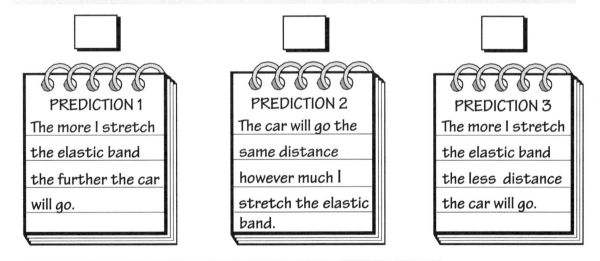

PREDICTION 1	PREDICTION 2	PREDICTION 3
The more I stretch the elastic band the further the car will go.	The car will go the same distance however much I stretch the elastic band.	The more I stretch the elastic band the less distance the car will go.

b)   (Circle) whether you guessed the right result on page 19.

 NO I DIDN'T.   YES I DID.

A final stunning elastic joke — oops, no space...

The results you get from experiments can be confusing at first.
Putting them into a table or bar chart makes it easier to see a pattern.

Making a Concept Map

A concept map is an excellent way of linking up lots of facts and ideas.

Q1 This concept map is about guinea pigs and rabbits. Use the map to decide whether the sentences below are true or false. Put ticks (✓) and crosses (✗) in the right boxes.

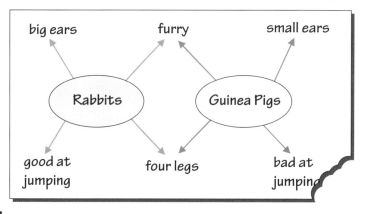

Rabbits are good at the bongos.

☐ Guinea pigs and rabbits are good at jumping.

☐ Guinea pigs are furry.

☐ Guinea pigs have big ears.

☐ Rabbits and guinea pigs are furry.

Q2 This concept map is about cats and dogs. Fill in the gaps using words from the box.

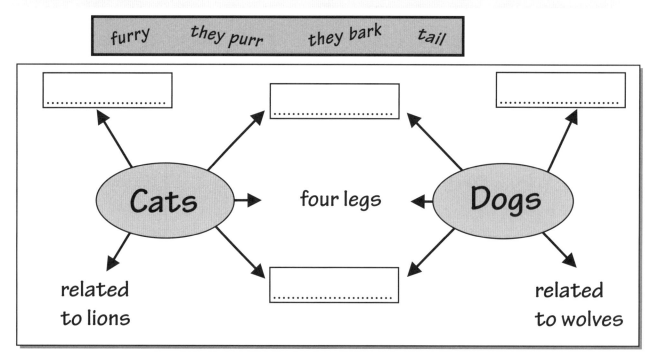

Here be dragons — but I know a short cut...

'Concept map' is a strange name, but a simple idea. Concept maps show how ideas link up between different things — 'kinda neat' (if you use 1980's American slang.)

A Forces Concept Map

You can check what you know about magnets and springs with a concept map.

Q1 Fill in the gaps in this concept map about pushes and pulls.
Use **all** the words written on the forehead of spatula-headed Peter.

This means squashing something.

SPATULA-HEADED PETER

repel   opposite   attract   compress

pulls   magnets   pushes   forces

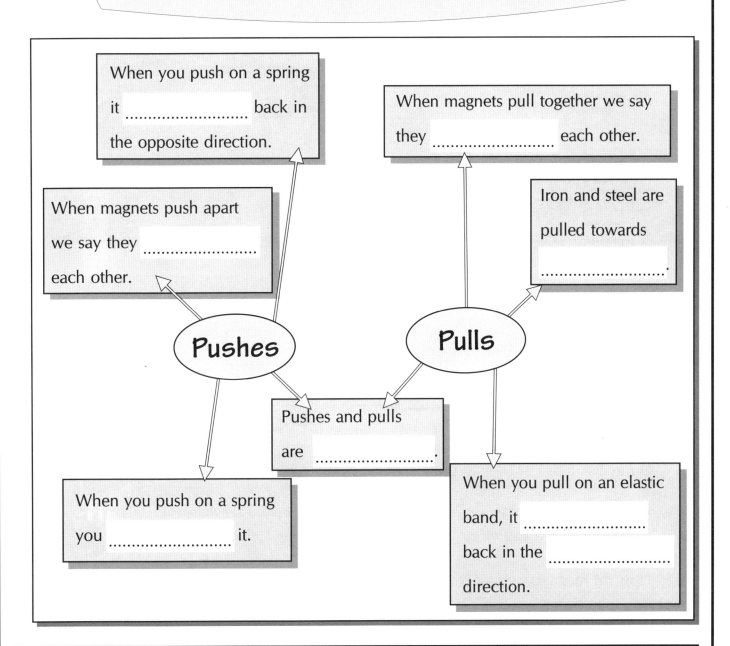

When you push on a spring it .... back in the opposite direction.

When magnets pull together we say they .... each other.

When magnets push apart we say they .... each other.

Iron and steel are pulled towards ....

Pushes

Pulls

Pushes and pulls are ....

When you push on a spring you .... it.

When you pull on an elastic band, it .... back in the .... direction.

I can't do a concept map — I don't know the way...

Concept maps can be all sorts of funny shapes and colours. Have a crack at doing some yourself — use colours, pictures, words and arrows to show how ideas fit together.

24

Revision Questions

Only two more pages to go. If you can answer all these then you really are sorted.
Don't worry if you get stuck — just look back through the book.

Q1 Finish the sentences below using some of the words from the splat below.

Forces ...push... or ...pull... .
They only act in one ...direction... .

PULL DIRECTION
PUSH DANCE

Q2 Write down whether the magnets are 'attracting' or 'repelling' each other.

The magnets are
...Repeling...
each other.

The magnets are
...attracting...
each other.

Q3 How do you tell if something is magnetic or not?
Circle the correct words in the brackets.

A magnetic material will (MOVE TOWARDS / MOVE AWAY FROM) a magnet.

Q4 Put a tick (✓) next to each magnetic thing below.

Flower [ ]

Iron screw [✓]

Trainers [ ]

Steel can [ ]

Q5 Write TRUE or FALSE after these sentences about magnetic metals.

All metals are magnetic. ...FALSE...   Iron and steel are magnetic. ...TRUE...
Some metals are magnetic. ...TRUE...   Copper and aluminium are magnetic. ...FLASE...

Q6 How do magnets help us to recycle metals?

....

Magnet Thatcher — the iron lady...

There are a fair few questions crammed on to this page. But don't panic — the answers
are all somewhere in the book. A good excuse to read all those lovely pages again.

© CGP 2003

Revision Questions

I bet you've had enough of springs and magnets by now. But just do this last page to officially make yourself an expert — then take a well-earned rest.

Q7 Give two examples of how we use springs in everyday life.

....

....

Q8 Use arrows to draw the direction of the forces in the pictures. Then finish the sentences using words from the box.

When the hand .... up on the spring, the spring

pulls .... on the hand.

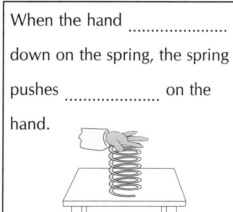

When the hand ....

down on the spring, the spring

pushes .... on the

hand.

PUSHES
UP
PULLS
DOWN

Q9 Draw arrows on the picture below to show the forces at work. Then circle the right words in brackets to finish the sentences.

a) The forces are (PUSH / PULL) forces.

b) The further the band is stretched, the (BIGGER / SMALLER) its force will be.

Gerald decided it was time for some spring cleaning.

Q10 Put a tick by the car which will go the furthest.

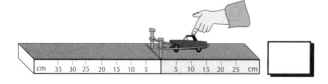

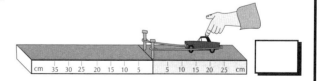

Don't "force" me to write another joke...

The jokes are getting terrible and you know everything there is to know about magnets and springs — it must finally be the end of the book. PHEW.

Index